ISBN: 978-0-9989943-4-5

Illustrated by Sheria Gregory

To contact the author, please email: 8Nationbooks@gmail.com

"I can do all things through Christ who strengthens me."

Philippians 4:13 NKJV

" If you have a dream, don't let anybody take it away, and always believe that the impossible is possible. "

Selena Quintanilla-Pérez

One sunny afternoon Sou set out to start her day. She thought to herself, what should I do today? I can bake a cake or maybe sit by the lake, all while wearing my favorite cape.

S
MY FAVORITE
Princess
SUE

What should I do? Oh, where do I start? What shall I do before it gets dark?

Pick up my toys or
pick on the boys?
Should I find my dad
or my mom instead?

Mom and dad, I found you both! "What should I do with my afternoon?"

family.

"Draw me a picture or maybe a few. Whatever you believe in your mind, you can do." Sou pondered and wondered for a few. What do I believe I can do?

I can fly a spaceship or
create an invention. How
about I become a President
fighting for human
connections?

VOTE

Sou began to draw,
drawing well into the
night.

"I can't believe I spent the whole day drawing ideas from my head."

Mommy laughed and said, "Soon you will spend your day fulfilling the ideas you drew today. This is only a start. There's a reason God blessed you with ideas from your heart."

You see, Sou only
needed to see what
was already inside.
Mommy tucked her in
bed and gave her a kiss.
"Good night!"

As Sou fell asleep, she
began to dream about all
the things she believed she
could do.
She said to herself,
"Tomorrow I know exactly
what I'll do."

Just like Sou, there
is nothing you, my
friend, cannot do.

What do you believe you can do?

My name is ______________________________

I believe I can ___________________________

Draw a picture:

CPSIA information can be obtained
at www.ICGtesting.com
Printed in the USA
BVRC101334240522
637945BV00003B/66